Contents

Levels*	Title	Composer	Page
G S	**Catching Snowflakes**	Colin Tommis	2
G S	**Rock Bottom**	Richard Wright	4
G (S)	**Summerhouse Waltz**	Stephen Goss	5
G G	**Leaves in the Breeze**	Derek Hasted	6
G G	**Musette** from English Suite No. 3, BWV 808	J. S. Bach arr. Richard Wright	7
G G	**Sleepy Joe's**	Jane Bentley	8
G G	**The Haunted House**	Stephen Goss	9
G P	**Not Another Waltz!**	Bob Power	10
G P	**Morning Song**	Richard Wright	11
G S (S)	**Menuett** from Baryton Trio, Hob. XI/27	Haydn arr. Christopher Susans	12
G G (S)	**Hopping Dance**	Stephen Kenyon	13
G G G	**No More School**	Colin Tommis	14
G G G	**Japanese Knotweed**	Jane Bentley	15
G G (G)	**Skating**	Colin Downs	16
G G P	**El rossinyol**	Trad. Catalan arr. Jonathan Leathwood	18
G S S (S)	**Dreamtime**	Bob Power	20
G G (S) (S)	**Brief Meditation**	Jane Bentley	21
G G G G	**Sword Dance**	Jonathan Leathwood	22
G G G G	**The Empty Castle**	Christopher Susans	24
G G P P	**Hot Wired**	Colin Tommis	26

*S = silver; G = gold; P = platinum; ( ) = the line must be played but cannot be assessed for a Medal.

In this book, all harmonics are natural and notated at sounding pitch.

Catching Snowflakes

Colin Tommis

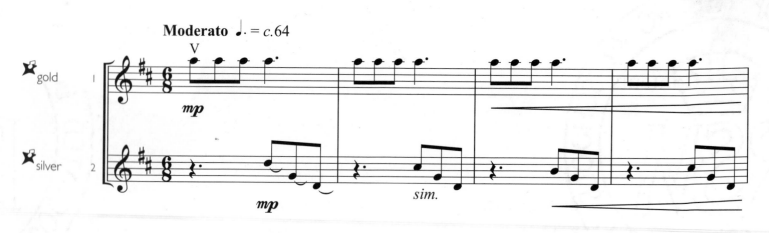

AB 3041

Rock Bottom

Richard Wright

AB 3041

Summerhouse Waltz

Stephen Goss

AB 3041

5

Leaves in the Breeze

Derek Hasted

AB 3041

Musette

from English Suite No. 3, BWV 808

J. S. Bach arr. Richard Wright

AB 3041

Sleepy Joe's

Jane Bentley

AB 3041

The Haunted House

Stephen Goss

Not Another Waltz!

Bob Power

AB 3041

Morning Song

Richard Wright

AB 3041

Menuett

from Baryton Trio, Hob. XI/27

Haydn arr. Christopher Susans

AB 3041

Hopping Dance

Stephen Kenyon

No More School

Colin Tommis

AB 3041

for Wills

Japanese Knotweed

Jane Bentley

* Weave a cocktail stick in between the top four strings, near the bridge.

↻ = Snap pizzicato: pull the string away from the fingerboard, between thumb and index finger, then let go so it snaps back.

Skating

Colin Downs

AB 3041

for my sister

El rossinyol

Trad. Catalan arr. Jonathan Leathwood

The title means 'The Nightingale'.

AB 3041

Dreamtime

Bob Power

AB 3041

Brief Meditation

Jane Bentley

* To bring the piece to a close, play C – with *dim. poco a poco* instead of *cresc. poco a poco* – followed by B and A.

× and ⌢ = finger cymbals. Suspend a pair of finger cymbals from the side of guitar 4's music stand nearest to guitar 3, so that they are within easy reach of both players. The 'struck' cymbal should hang just below the stand and the 'beater' cymbal much lower down.

AB 3041

for Heidi

Sword Dance

Jonathan Leathwood

AB 3041

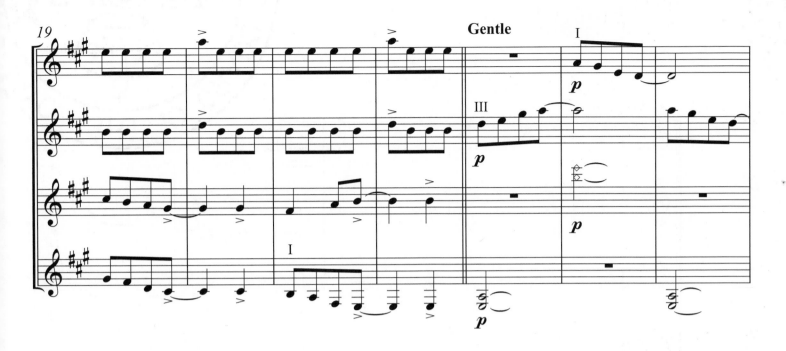

Gentle

Building to the end

The Empty Castle

Christopher Susans

AB 3041

Hot Wired

Colin Tommis

AB 3041